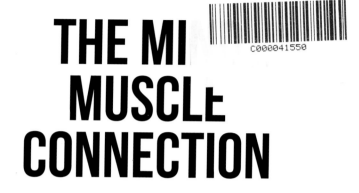

# THE MIND MUSCLE CONNECTION

By Rob Harris

This book is dedicated to
the only Mum I ever needed.

# CONTENTS

First Published 2014 by Rob Harris     © 2014 Rob Harris

# ROB HARRIS

Look beneath the superficial cover of skin and sweat and you'll soon find that exercise is one of the most powerful tools known to humankind. It doesn't just shape and prime the body, but also sharpen and support the mind.

The lessons learnt whilst under a barbell, pounding the tarmac or pushing out one more rep than you've ever done before can carry over into almost every other area of life. At the same time that you lift a weight, you lift yourself. Increasing your heart rate increases your speed of thought. Reps beget resilience. Seeing your actions and choices manifested as results within your own body gives cast iron reassurance of the relationship between intelligent effort and reward.

Looking for the spark? The Mind-Muscle Connection will give you the direction, motivation and impetus to get on the right track. Your body - the only one you'll ever have - is your responsibility. Responsibility isn't a problem, it's an opportunity to take control - and control means results. Seize the opportunity now to make a difference and you'll soon be reaping more than just visual rewards.

This collection of thoughts from gym floor will get you Pumped!

SOME
SAY.
SOME

# MOTIVATION & MINDSET

# NEW START

Before you **GET** anything you must first **TRY**.

You may want more money - get a job. Any job.
Want more money? Work harder, get a second job.

Want more success? Look at your failures and **DON'T** repeat them and work harder.

Want a physique you are really proud of? Then you must **TRY**. **NOTHING** happens by itself. **YOU** must make it happen. If you try you give yourself a chance. If you don't try then you have nothing more than regrets and wasted time. Even a marathon begins with one step. It's down to no one else but you to turn your hopes and dreams into a reality.

The most important step toward anything is the first. Inception. You have to 'start' to give yourself the opportunity 'finish'.

**Find yourself failing more than succeeding?**

**Losing more than winning?**

**Spending more than earning?**

**Frowning more than smiling?**

If what you're doing isn't working - do something different! Think **'CAN'** more than 'can't'. **'WILL'** more than 'won't'. Regardless of your circumstances or experiences - only you choose your attitude.

You have a greater impact on others than you think. When asked how you are swap the 'Not too bad' greetings for 'Getting there!', 'I'm good' or 'Yeah, fine' and see how much better people respond to you. No one welcomes negativity into their lives - so don't force it on people.

# CHOOSE POSITIVITY OR YOU'RE CHOOSING FAILURE.

# CHOICE, NOT CHANCE, DETERMINES RESULTS.

The single most potent and effective weapon at your disposal to improve yourself CAN'T be bought. It CAN'T be found in a tub, in a pill, in a pin, online or from a friend. It CAN'T be bottled and it CAN'T be stored, yet it's with you 24/7/365. It CAN be used anywhere and has amazing capabilities when applied with consistent determination, effort and knowledge. The weapon has already been paid for and is at your command and is capable of things you have only yet dreamt of.

The weapon?

 **THE WEAPON IS YOU**

We all have strengths and weaknesses. Don't let your weaknesses mask or undermine your strengths! Manage your weaknesses and minimise their impact. When it comes to creating the physique you want - if your weakness is chocolate/biscuits/crisps then don't have them easily to hand! Don't have them in your home, glove box or desk at work. You have to earn them!

If your weakness is missing out cardio in the gym then do it outside. Walk the dog, push a push chair, swim, cycle, just MOVE.

If your weakness is not working certain body parts (legs anyone?) then do them first in the week and free style each workout using different exercises and reps each time, so you're not daunted by having to do the same thing each time. You're capable of far more than you have ever dreamed. Start NOW!

reSULTS ARE THE CONSEQUENCE of CHOICES

It's not rocket science! Changing your body shape/composition/fat levels is as simple as lifting metal up and down (resistance training), putting one foot in front of the other (cardio) and eating suitable amounts of suitable foods at suitable times (nutrition). DO NOT think that this is beyond you. The only barrier to this is your mind. Leave "can't" out of the equation, leave "won't" at home and don't invite "should have/ could have /would have" to the party. Make a logical plan and execute it. If you don't know what to do - get help, then execute it. RESULTS are the consequence of CHOICES.

**The first 6 months are complete, half the year has passed - how's the New Years Resolutions looking now?**

If over the last 6 months you've consistently stopped sets due to mild discomfort. How do you feel now?

If you've consistently thought about doing cardio, but instead gone home to watch TV. How does it feel now?

If you had plans for a 6 pack and 'ripping up' this summer but you proved too weak to not consume an excess of chocolate/take away/alcohol. How does it feel now?

Every time you opt for a short cut, every time you give in, every time you miss an opportunity to improve, you are cheating yourself and losing ground on the 'You' that you could be!

# 'I DID' IS MUCH MORE REWARDING THAN 'I WISH' OR 'I SHOULD HAVE/ WOULD HAVE/ COULD HAVE.

**If you have negative lifestyle factors affecting your goals - DON'T cling on to them!**

The couple of beers EVERY night is helping to keep you fat, the missing the gym to watch TV is doing NOTHING to reduce your blood pressure, the all too regular fast food is NOT the protein your body needs to repair.

Realise that you don't NEED to do these things and realise they are only acting to hold YOU back. You must make simple, yet smart, choices if you actually want to achieve the things you say you do.

"What CAN you do?" doesn't need to be so different from "What you WILL do". You may not be able to run 100m in under 10 seconds or a mile in under 4 minutes but you CAN make a difference. You CAN make a difference to yourself, your health, self confidence and performance. You CAN inspire those around you to make smart decisions and improve themselves. You CAN do your part to make this nation healthy and take the strain off the NHS with less money wasted on treating diseases caused by overindulgence. Convert POTENTIAL into REALITY, it just takes 'I WILL' power.

There are no magic supplements. There is no secret combination of sets and reps. Drugs may help some with short term gains, but show me a drug without side effects. The real magic lies within the changes you can bring about both physically and mentally in yourself, the secret is hard work and the best drug... is exercise!

**"It was raining"**

**"I only had an hour"**

**"I was tired"**

**"There was something on telly"**

Watching the coverage of the paralympic swimming in 2012, reinforced how lame some of the excuses I've heard are and how inspirational the athletes are. You're capable of more than you think! Exchange your words for deeds and your thoughts for actions and you'll convert your hopes to results.

Modern life dictates that we're faced with decisions at every turn, Blackberry or iPhone? Petrol or Diesel? Stay in or go out? When it comes to our health and physiques we can make smart choices at each turn that will help us continue toward our goals. Here are some commonly stated problems and some 'Smart' solutions:-

- **Late night cravings** - Instead of reaching for the biscuits or cake have some sweet flavoured protein (Rocky Road, Cookies & Cream, Chocolate Peanut Butter) ready made and frozen to eat like an ice cream. Other options include a serving of Muscle Mousse, a protein shake with a couple tea spoons of nut butter, a serving of Quark with protein powder stirred in to flavour.

- **Time constraints limiting workouts per week** - Don't do single body parts per workout if you think you might only be able to train twice in a week. Hit the lower body (eg Squats/Press/Lunge/Calves) in one workout then the upper (Shoulder Press/Chin Ups/Bench Press/Deadlifts/Dips) in the next. If you only make it twice you've still worked all muscle groups. If you do happen to be able to make it a third time then you can hit the first workout again.

- **Eating out** - Socialising and enjoying time with friends is a great de-stressor and doesn't have to be eliminated just because you workout! If it's been a considerable amount of time since you last had a treat meal, then eat whatever you want. If the meal is part of a structured eating plan and you don't want to stray too far then choose to skip the starter or pick a salad. Choose a main course based around chicken or fish or a high protein vegetarian choice. Dessert is your choice, but I find I'd rather have dessert (and therefore still eating along with my companions at the end of the meal, as opposed to finishing before and watching others eat!) than a starter. Still, don't go overboard here. For beverages choose cordials, diet sodas, water, black coffee, green tea.

- **Can't get to the gym, but need to do cardio** - Walk! Anywhere! On your own, with your partner, with your kids, with a dog- any dog! Just move.

Sometimes circumstances can make it difficult to see the 'light at the end of the tunnel'.

## CHECK LIST.

### Are you facing the right way?
The direction you are facing is more important than your speed of movement.

### Are you in the right tunnel?
Pick the correct path to reach your destination.

### Are your eyes even open?
This seems too obvious yet often the path to your goal is right in front of you. The 'Light' is there, see it and move toward it!

# ENCOURAGEMENT IS UNDERRATED

Remember how good it felt when a teacher said something positive in one of your school reports? How good it feels when someone compliments your work? When someone tells you 'You CAN do it'? Encouragement works, it drives, it motivates, and it improves application and consistency. Ever noticed how often the crowd getting behind a football team can improve their performance? The chances are if you encourage others, you too will experience benefits. Not only does it feel good to encourage others and see their results, but it's more likely they will then reciprocate and send encouragement your way.

# THE DRAG EFFECT

Through the years I've spent in gyms there's a phenomenon I've frequently observed. I call it **'The Drag Effect'**. The first gym I trained at was based in a leisure centre, the dumbbells went up to 22kg, so when I was using the 14kg dumbbells I thought I was doing pretty well. When I saw older guys hoisting the 18kg dumbbells it blew my mind. I thought it was incredible!

When I moved away to University the gym there had 40kg dumbbells, thus making my 14kg lifts look puny. I resolved to redouble my efforts, strive to improve and break all previous records. Within weeks I'd doubled many of my lifts, set new records and was experiencing gains like never before.  Now why did this happen? I'd not even maxed out the dumbbells in the leisure centre, yet moving to the new facility brought results and progress I had only dreamt about. Training at the University gym meant I was surrounded by a greater number of dedicated, focussed and advanced trainees. This inspired, motivated and 'dragged' me along far faster than I'd been progressing at the leisure centre. I was now determined to emulate and then surpass the people now training all around me.

After leaving Uni I moved abroad to work in a gym which was incredibly well equipped, with dumbbells up to 62.5kg. Again, very quickly, I saw rapid improvements. Each workout I was surrounded by larger, more advanced trainees and again this pulled me along to strive for more, to work harder and push to break all barriers. Training at a facility with advanced equipment and advanced members is one of the quickest ways to push your own boundaries. Another is to link up with a training partner who is superior to you in the areas you wish to improve; this may be strength, size or body composition. They will 'drag' you along much quicker than if you toil on your own. Combine a quality gym, a motivated/advanced training partner and your own effort and intensity and you can't fail to improve!

As a gym owner I hear a fair amount of *"I'll start back Monday"*, *"I'll start back when the kids go back to school"* and the popular *"I'll start back in the New Year"*.

Invariably events do occur that may mean you MUST take a break from training. That's life. Yet too often too long is taken to restart, time is wasted, excessive regression takes hold. Leading to being even more disheartened when exercise is finally resumed. The chances are without the 'keystone' of exercise in place all other factors - food selection, sleep quality, smoking/drinking habits will worsen. If you've had a enforced break from training and are able to start back - START NOW. Don't wait until next Monday, next week, next year! See what you can achieve in the time you would of otherwise wasted!

You might be tired.
It may be dark outside
and cold, it might be
another day of work for you,
but remember you have a
massive advantage.
You're ALIVE!
Carpe diem.

IF YOU TOOK JUST
HALF THE TIME YOU
SPEND THINKING
YOU 'CAN'T'
AND USED IT DOING
WHAT IT TAKES
SO THAT YOU 'CAN'
YOU WOULD BE
AMAZED AT
THE RESULTS

# CHOICES MAKE CHANGES!

Choose form over weight.

Choose feel over numbers.

Choose food over supplements.

Choose quality over quantity.

Choose intensity over gear.

Choose sleep over caffeine.

Choose water over fizzy drinks.

Choose knowledge over ignorance.

# THE CHOICES YOU MAKE DICTATE THE RESULTS YOU GET. CHOOSE WISELY!

Complaining is easy, anyone can do it! What does it achieve apart from reinforcing negativity in the mind and infesting others with your negativity?

There will always be Mondays, it will always be cold in winter in England and there will always be people with more money than you. Focussing on the negative will not make it a positive.

If you don't like waking up in the morning - give yourself something to look forward to! A fresh, tasty breakfast can make emerging from sleep a pleasure. Working out can also ready your body for the day ahead and increase energy levels. Try a morning fat burning blast and you'll be impressed with how much more awake you feel afterwards.

If you don't like the cold treat yourself to some extra warm clothing and drink plenty of water and eat regularly to keep your metabolism stoked. Also set aside a savings tin to put money in for your next holiday; Every time you feel like complaining about the cold do something productive instead and put £5 in the tin. If you're English you'll have the holiday saved for by the end of the week!

Truly successful people don't waste time complaining. They use that time to KEEP DOING what makes them successful!

# THE HUMBLE WORK OUT

'Me time'.

A daily focal point.

A potent way to de-stress.

Something to take pride in.

A time to look forward to.

A goal at the end of your working day.

An awesome way to protect and improve health.

A means to shape your body with your own will.

An addiction actually worth having!

**Nobody can ever take a work out away from you!
When's your next fix?**

As I watch a.n.o.t.h.e.r. member step on to the weighing scales I still don't get it. I've been watching gym-goers and dieters weigh themselves for well over a decade and it still baffles me.

If you're looking to lose fat and the scales say you're lighter, is this a good thing? What if you haven't lost fat. What if you've lost muscle? What if you're dehydrated? It's ok right, because the scales say you're lighter! But wait, did you want to be lighter or lose fat? The two do not necessarily go hand in hand.

If you're looking to build muscle and the scales say you're heavier is this a good thing? What if you're just adding fat? What if you're just holding more water. It's ok, right, because the scales say you're heavier. But wait, did you want to be heavier or more muscular? Being heavier does not necessarily mean you are more muscular!

If you truly want to know if your training is effective and if you're heading towards your goals then combine tape measurements, pictures and occasionally body weight. Of course this will take more effort than just weighing yourself, but it's truly worth it.

# BELIEVING IS SEEING!

When it comes to transforming your physique/losing body fat/'toning' up/ getting 'hench' - You must first see in your mind what you want to see in the mirror!

I've been training for over a decade now and wanted to share with you some of the mistakes I've made so that you can avoid making them yourself. Henry Ford said *"The only real mistake is the one from which we learn nothing"*. Often I've learnt more from my mistakes than I have from any smooth period of training.

1. **Underestimate the importance of warming up and preparation at your peril.** Warming up doesn't have to mean 10 minutes of cardio. Simply rotating the shoulders forward and backward 20 times can help increase the temperature of the surrounding tissues and reduce the chance of injury. If you're about to chin your own bodyweight it makes sense to do some light curls to prepare your biceps. Trust me - It's better to spend 90 seconds warming up than 90 days injured. Preparation can also improve performance - early, lighter sets can help 'grease' the movement for later, heavier max sets. You're not a machine and it pays to reacquaint yourself with a movement with lighter sets prior to heavy ones. Every injury I've had has taught me more about my body.

2. **Don't knock it until you've tried it.** 7 years ago I used to mock another PT for using a foam roller. *'If it's not a barbell or dumbbell then what's the use?'* I used to think. Foam rolling now plays an integral role in my prehab/rehab routine and significantly reduces any recovery time from a strain. Don't be closed minded, try different styles of training and different approaches to other aspects of fitness.

3. **Don't judge your results by your bodyweight.** Don't get me wrong - I've fallen into this trap myself more than once. If you're trying to look better then don't judge your progress on how heavy/ light you are, judge it on how you LOOK! Your body weight will tell you far less about how you look than a set of progress pictures (obviously). Sure stepping on the scales is easy - but then 'easy' rarely achieves anything. Take pictures, take measurements and occasionally take your weight also.

4. **Don't think 'Bulking'; rather think 'Muscle building'.** Just because you're not focussing on getting leaner doesn't mean you should take the hand brake off fat gain. The simple truth is if you eat junk you will look like junk. Only the very young or very fortunate can get away with eating high levels of junk food and not gaining body fat. The premise that eating large amounts of junk food  because 'it's just more calories and I'm bulking' is flawed. Muscle building, for the most part, requires regular intake of high quality proteins, unprocessed carbs and healthy fats, not thrice weekly fast food burgers! Every junk meal eaten is a missed opportunity to eat quality foods and build more muscle.

5.  **Knowing your actual goal.** How can you know what actions to take regarding food or exercise if you don't know where you want to get to (or where you're starting from!)? Getting pictures and measurements taken will certainly help here.

6.  **Food shop to be prepared.** If you don't have the right food for the right situation at the right time at your finger tips you will be tempted to miss a meal or even worse to eat the 'wrong' thing. How often have you been hungry at a garage or service station or checkout and picked up something you later regretted? Make sure your shopping and cooking ensure you always have what you need to eat to hand.

7.  **Keep a training log.** This will be the single best training partner you ever have. It will always turn up, it will always tell you the absolute truth and it will always be factual! Write down exercises, weights used and reps as essentials. Rest periods, drop sets etc can also be included. Be accountable to yourself.

8.  **Do your best. No one else can do it for you!** Sometimes things are easy and sometimes things are difficult but it's the difficult times and events that matter most in the long run and teach us more about ourselves. Regardless if something is easy, difficult, daunting or simple you must give it your best to get the best outcome.

'**Reasons**' are one thing and '**Excuses**' are distinctly another. Make sure you know the difference. Reasons are facts. Excuses are white lies to yourself. If you've made it clear to yourself that you have goals yet have made excuses to miss a workout then you're lying to yourself.

Challenges are part and parcel of life - just surviving until birth is a challenge itself! Challenges can come and appear in many guises and can be minor inconveniences or major barriers. Challenges can sometimes be self-imposed and sometimes others are responsible for burdening us with difficulty. There is one thing that we do and get to choose and that's how we respond to each challenge we face and it's this response which dictates the true effect of the challenge upon us.

With this choice we have in mind I wanted to share a few tips for getting over/around/through a barrier that may be imposed on you. Firstly, imagine you have an injury to a muscle or joint. This is one of the prime reasons why many people stop training completely. Obviously a complete rest is necessary in the acute phase of a major break or tear. As soon as the acute phase has passed it's time to think about rehabbing the injury - consult with an injury professional, structure a rehab plan and begin to execute it. As soon as you can return to training start with working the body parts that aren't affected, you may have to reduce the weight you use and modify the movement but just start! You'll soon begin to regain strength and realise that how you felt when the injury happened isn't a permanent state of mind!

Sometimes something as simple as the weather can make us feel like staying at home and not venturing out, so a workout might get missed. If, occasionally, you don't want to leave the house due to thunder, torrential rain, snow, etc then stay home. Get your food cooked for the next few days, this can be a real help when it comes to saving time and fitting in your meals around life!

A busy gym can throw a spanner in the works when it comes to following a set routine, but there are ways and means to avoid disappointment. Try training an hour earlier or later, or in the morning. Try training on different days or splitting your routine so that you aren't training chest on a Monday! If after all these ideas you still think that you're not finding the space/equipment you need - look to introduce an element of 'freestyle' to your workout - complete the moves/exercises that you can and then use whatever else is free as a replacement for things that are busy.

# ATTITUDE. YOUR CHOICE!

If you're a complete novice or returning to training then you may be able to see up to 10kg improvements in just a week with large, compound movements. However, if you've been training consistently for some time then you're doing well if you can still add 1kg to the bar, on ANY lift, EVERY week.

Such small, incremental improvements can often be overlooked as insignificant. Do not dismiss small steps forward. ANY forward movement is progress.

The single most dramatic/important/decisive improvement you can make is beyond simply battling with gravity and is not limited to kgs or lbs. It is to choose a positive attitude. This will enable you to do more, in less time, than you ever imagined.

A positive attitude can be the deciding factor on whether you choose to hit the gym or hit the couch, whether you just attempt a personal best or smash a personal best or if you see something as an impossible barrier or merely another hurdle to leap.

# WHEN YOU WANT SOMETHING BADLY ENOUGH... YOU'LL WAIT AND WORK... AND WORK AND WAIT... AND WORK SOME MORE.

# YOU'RE ALWAYS MORE LIKELY TO SUCCEED IF YOU 1. START. AND 2. BELIEVE.

# HONESTY IS THE BEST POLICY

Even more so when it applies to yourself. If you can't be honest with yourself it's highly likely you'll struggle to be honest with others. When it comes to training and nutrition lying to yourself will waste your efforts and will also waste the most important of commodities - time.

Be honest, are you eating as cleanly as you can? How many packs of crisps/chocolate bars are you eating per week? Is it occasional or is it actually most days? Are take-away meals more regular than you report to your PT? Are your alcohol units adding up to more than you're willing to admit to yourself? Be honest! Are you kidding yourself about how much junk you do eat, or how much nutritious food you actually eat?

Do you honestly think the 10 minutes of warm-up CV constitutes what is necessary to rev your metabolism to lower your body fat? Is your range of motion when training compromised to allow you to lift a little more weight? Is your technique 'honest'? Are you working your target muscle with each exercise or merely your ego? Are you training intensely enough to change your body, or just 'think' you are? Be honest!

Get real with yourself, be honest! If you can't, or won't, then look to someone else to appraise your lifting and nutrition.

The Inches YOU need are all around YOU. Get up, get your attitude set and get after the things you want. They're not going to find their way to you. You must relentlessly pursue them. 'I can't make you do it'- but you can.

# " WORDS ARE, OF COURSE, THE MOST POWERFUL DRUG USED BY MANKIND. "

*Rudyard Kipling*

Words are your daily weapon. Whether it is a goal or just a feeling you're pursuing - words can help or hinder your journey.

Consider this; If you keep repeating to yourself or others that you can't do something then it's likely that even you don't believe you can do it, if you don't believe it then you won't apply yourself, if you don't apply yourself then that thing you want simply won't happen. Now if you do keep repeating that you can do something then you're more likely to believe it, believing it will make you apply yourself and applying yourself will put you in a much better position to succeed.

Words carry a strong indicator of our feelings and beliefs. The person who tells me they are 'feeling good' and the next that tells me they are 'not too bad' typically mean the same thing - but the message carries a completely different feeling. It's in the words. Say it's time to come to work out and it's a seemingly monotonous 40 minutes of treadmill work on the menu. Phrases like that is bound to make it seem like a chore. Call it 'the next step', 'gut-blasting', 'fat-fighting' or 'getting me one step closer to my goal' and it becomes just that little bit easier, which is never a bad thing! Choose your words carefully and remember the strong link between words and thoughts.

**GYM MEMBERSHIP CARD**

**First Name:** Never
**Second Name:** Attend

There's something not quite right if you have membership to a gym but never go. Paying membership for months on end and not attending would have seemed ludicrous on the day you joined- and it should NOW!

I've got a plan for you - CANCEL THE MEMBERSHIP. No one wants to pay for something they don't use. Paying for a unused membership can lead to resentment toward the facility ("they kept taking my money"....well you didn't tell them not to and it's your choice how long you pay for!) but also toward exercise. Personally, as a gym owner you're my most frustrating member! There is an alternative. You've been off for some time so it's not going to be easy to return - but 'easy' is overrated so let's get stuck in!

1. Set yourself a start date, write it down, put it somewhere visible and tell people about it. This will create more of an

incentive to follow it through. Set yourself to attend the gym three times in the first week and do absolutely and completely whatever you want to do. YOU choose the activities, order and duration. If you want to do 'chest' three times then so be it - this week is less about perfection and more about starting to create a habit and making it easy to return.

Commit to not buying any more junk food and also start to eat your way through any that's left in your house. Once it's gone, it's gone! And the sooner the better.

2. With the first week complete make a plan to meet with your gym owner or a Personal Trainer. Get baseline pictures and measurements taken. Again commit to three sessions this week. Now put body parts in order Legs/Back/Chest/Shoulders/Bi's/Tri's and complete one exercise for each (3*12). No world record attempts, but increase weight through the sets until the last is challenging but that you can complete without a spotter and with immaculate form. After you complete the weights move on to some light cardio, but ensure when the 10 minutes are complete that you have a light sweat.

Again do not buy any more junk food. Instead celebrate committing your return to the gym by knowing you're doing something that will only ever benefit YOU. Also, on Friday or Saturday or Sunday enjoy a meal out or take away. This will give you something to focus on as you travel through the week and begin to miss 'treat food'

3. Week three and it's time to repeat the body part order from last week but challenge yourself to use different exercises this week. It doesn't matter that you're not sticking to a rigid plan- after having such a break just the introduction of ANY resistance exercise will make you stronger. For cardio your challenge is to complete three unconventional sessions. Ideally after each weights session either go and smash a oversized tyre with a hammer, go for a swim/cycle or run some light/basic intervals between lampposts (walk one, jog one).

4. Week four and the habit is beginning to solidify, you should now be looking forward to each session with fear/laziness receding into the distance. Get a exercise professional to structure a program made just for you. Get your measurements and pictures taken again. This week you will set baseline weights for each exercise and also look at maybe picking a training partner- you could even introduce someone new to the gym! Treat yourself to a new pair of trainers, vest, T-shirt or shorts.

You are now on track to reap all the benefits that exercise can bring. A stronger heart, lower blood pressure and a more efficient cardiovascular system. More energy to complete all of life's other tasks. Increased strength, lower body fat and more vitality will all be yours.

**What are you waiting for?**

# BUT I WANT EVERYTHING YESTERDAY!

I want to lose weight (replace with 'fat') without having to leave my chair, I want it to be easy, I want to do it fast, I want it to be painless, I don't want to sweat, I don't want to have to go to a gym, I don't want to have to work for it... blah blah blah.

Man/Woman up and put the time and effort in. Then, and only then, will you begin to get what you want.

# WORKING ACHIEVES WHAT WISHING WON'T

# 'ME TIME'

Work time, family time, commute time, coursework, housework, food shopping, DIY, gardening. There are many varied demands on our time. Amongst the many commitments 'Me Time' should not be undervalued or underestimated! Too often we're left doing tasks for everyone else, spending our time on things which build up tension and anxiety, with seemingly no respite. Forgetting to take time out for yourself is dangerous yet a common trap to fall into. Whilst you're ploughing on doing things for others and working through your own tasks it makes sense to schedule in some time for YOU. Keeping yourself sane, de-stressed and content with your own personal goals will make you more able to deal with everything else.

There's many things to use for 'Me Time', personally I've found that 99% of the time exercise is my favourite choice. Exercise is great for releasing pent up aggression - you can't 'hurt' the weights. Exercise is great for releasing tension - you control all the variables and choose what to do and how to do it. Exercise is always there and consistent - 100kg is always going to be 100kg, it can't be having a bad day. Wrapping your fingers around that dumbbell handle, that barbell or chin-up bar you know what you're going to get, how it's going to feel and that you'll feel better afterwards! Combining all the psychological benefits and all the physical benefits shows what a powerful weapon exercise is and that it's a worthy use of your 'Me Time'.

# STOP COMPLAINING

Through human interaction and the wonders of Facebook I hear someone complain about something they DON'T want to do every 34.6 seconds, on average.

"I don't want to drive there".
"I don't want to work there".
"I don't want to cut the grass".
"I don't want to do the housework".
"I don't want to get-up".

Sometimes we have to do things we don't want to do, SOMETIMES! The amount of time spent complaining about and then completing things you don't want to do seems illogical when there's many things you do want to do but won't do them!

"I want to lose weight".
"I want to earn more money".
"I want to visit a/b/c" are also heard but how many of these things will YOU do?

Spend more time focussing on doing things that will help you get what you WANT, not on the things you don't want to do. Get that qualification you need for the job you want, go and get the experience for the career you want - even if it means doing it for free for now and if you want to change your body you'd better start exercising and eating appropriately.

Cut the complaining, devise a plan (with help if needed) and execute it NOW. Time's ticking!

# NOW!
## DO IT NOW!
### NOT LATER. NOT 'IN A MINUTE'.
### NOT 'SOON'. NOT TOMORROW.

If you're not getting what you want you need to change your mindset NOW.

Start with the mind and all the necessary actions will fall into place. You need to BELIEVE you can do something, otherwise you won't commit yourself to the ACTIONS that are needed to get the RESULTS! If you know in your mind you can lose body fat then when the snack van comes a calling you won't be tempted to buy a pie/pasty/sausage roll, you won't be tempted into eating cake in the office or fast food at lunch time. If you believe you can lose body fat you will make time to get to the gym or another form of exercise. If you don't believe in the process you will find some excuse not to exercise.

Everything begins with the mind and belief in your ability to reach a goal.

# — BELIEF ▸ ACTIONS ▸ RESULTS —

...and there's only one person ever going to have the ability to choose your level of belief. YOU. Seize the opportunity.

You're planning on completing a 26.2 mile marathon in 6 months time, this is a large goal on a medium to long term basis. Should you focus your mind and energies on the last stride of the event, which completes the marathon? Alternatively should you put the majority of your energies into structuring your training/nutritional plan, the next training session and your meals for the next day?

**ALWAYS** keep your 'end goal' in the back of your mind, call it forward when motivation is flagging - BUT keep the majority of your focus on the NEXT step! If you don't take care of the next meal and the next training session there will be no reaching your end goal! Energy will be wasted and frustration at failure will build until the task is resented and abandoned.

Now go back and substitute YOUR goal into the opening paragraph. It can apply to any goal.

Focus on the day to day 'Process' of reaching your end goal, not the goal itself, and you'll be far more likely to get to where you want to be.

# MAKE IT
# HAPPEN

Often life throws up situations where what we already HAVE conflicts with what we actually WANT. Often we'll want more of something, ie money, sleep, holidays, though sometimes we want less of other things, ie work, body fat, commuting distance.

When this CONFLICT happens it can lead to two differing outcomes. Firstly, if you have conflict without the WILL to change then it will create frustration and resentment. If you want more money but aren't prepared to work more, acquire more training or work smarter then you won't earn more money. If you want more sleep but aren't prepared to sacrifice that shite late night TV program or an hour on Candy Crush then you won't get more sleep.

The second scenario still has conflict, but this time you have the will to CHANGE, this creates resolution and a movement beyond the dilemma. Want to save more money? So you stop making impulse purchases and start a savings account - then it can happen. Want to be leaner? So you improve your nutrition and exercise habits - then it will happen.

The difference between what you have and what you want is often the WILL to make it happen. Stop complaining and start DOING.

Ever got in your car and not known where you were driving to? Yes? Me too. I used to use random/aimless driving to help break up the monotony of A-Level revision. 4 hours learning about mitosis and meiosis and then it was out into my B reg, Renault 5, 1.0 litre for 30 minutes of down time to give my brain a break from learning. Now this, for me, was the exception. 99% of the time I have a direction to head in and a goal to reach. This makes the cost of the fuel and the use of my time justifiable and productive!

Once we've reached our primary destination, then what? Well the chances are you are either there for business, social, domestic or pleasure reasons. And after that? Of course you'll either drive home, or back to work or to some other predetermined destination. The point is this; Goals are the same as destinations and goals rock! Goals, like trying to reach a destination, are great as they focus our attention and efforts, increase direction, commitment and determination. Yet reaching one goal and then floundering/procrastinating without setting another goal will see you slip back to where you were originally.

Once a goal is set, you will then be able to construct a plan to reach that goal and then execute the plan. Now once this initial goal has been reached you need to follow up with a second goal. It could be having a period of relaxation, to iron out any niggles and feel recovered. So this might mean planning a week off training, a sports massage and committing to a week of early nights. Often though it will mean assessing yourself again and decided what you now want to work on, having achieved the previous targets. So say you wanted to lose 2 stone of fat and then go about successfully achieving it. Once this goal is reached you should immediately decide on the next goal/destination or you'll begin to regress. For example, you might then decide you want to focus on building strength to be able to Bench Press/Squat/Deadlift certain weights, so now your training would centre around Power lifting techniques and becoming stronger. This will again give you a direction to head in, you can then formulate a plan and execute the plan with focus and intensity.

To ensure continuing progress and to keep you focused it's important to remember that goals need to be followed by more goals!

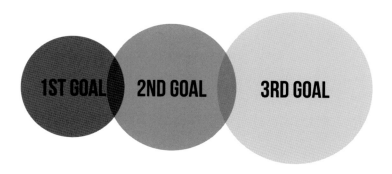

# SSSSHHHH, NO ONE WILL EVER KNOW

No one will know if you don't train legs, as long as you wear trackies. No one will ever know if you keep eating junk food to excess, as long as you keep wearing baggy clothes. No one will ever know if you keep avoiding cardio, as long as you keep covered up. No one will ever know if you keep using lat pull downs instead of chin ups/leg extensions instead of squats/seated rows instead of barbell rows/etc, as long as you keep undercover. No one will ever know if you keep training chest/arms more than all other larger body parts, as long as you can blame your posture on working at a desk.

No one will know (maybe!), except **YOU!**

Be aware of what your goals really are and shape your training and nutrition around them. Don't take the easy route out, it WASTES TIME and effort. Do push yourself to be the best that you can be, at every chance!

Weightlifting comes in many forms; Bodybuilding, Powerlifting and Olympic lifting being the main disciplines. When performed correctly, weightlifting can teach us many things about HONESTY. This is down to the consistency of gravity. It's unwavering and unrelenting consistency means 40kg will always be 40kg. You can't LIE or DECEIVE your body that 40kg will ever weigh lighter. Lift 40kg one week and try 60kg the next week and its not going to happen. Gravity will not let you.

Weightlifting performed correctly reinforces the relationship between effort, work, consistency and REWARD. If you focus and commit time and effort you will be rewarded with results. You can't STEAL results. There's a true satisfaction in knowing that you have honestly EARNED whats yours. Forget the police, court, prison - one day you will have to face YOURSELF. Are you ready?

There's a brotherhood between those that regularly lift, a mutual respect, concern and bond. Need a spot, its there. Need positive encouragement, its there. Need ideas for new exercises, its there. When you have this network you know you only have to ask for what you want, not STEAL from others. After all it takes a bigger man to admit they need help and ask for what they want. Stealing is for the weak. Stealing is so unrewarding that the high fades as quickly as the loot is frittered away, hence the high rate of repeat offenders. Get a job.

# WANT TO BE TALLER? OVER 23? TOUGH.

# WANT TO BE LEANER?

# WANT TO BE STRONGER?

# WANT TO BE MORE MUSCULAR?

# WANT A STRONGER HEART?

# WANT MORE LUNG POWER?

___

It's there, IF you really, honestly, truly want it. That's all you got to do - WANT it. If you want it you can get it.

___

Think it's too difficult, you got too much on, not enough time, starting too far back, genetics not good enough?

Think AGAIN. If the abundance of people around you and online that get what YOU want isn't a powerful enough indicator that YOU too can get it then I've got a plan for you.

Start. Not tomorrow. Not after your next holiday. Not in the New Year. Start NOW. Give it 2 weeks on a personalised nutrition plan and workout program and you WILL start to BELIEVE.

But what can you do now, on a Sunday afternoon?
Let's break this down.

1. First must be your mindset. You must COMMIT to making the changes required to get the results you want. FLICK THE SWITCH in your mind. KNOW that it's possible. BELIEVE that you have the ability to get what you want and the only thing that now stands in your way is a series of small, manageable, achievable steps. These steps are THE only thing in your way - but they are not an obstacle, they are your route.

2. Second begin accumulating the information you need to reach your goal. The internet, books, magazines and fitness professionals will have more information than you can possibly need. Begin by sifting through until you find someone's opinion that makes sense and you trust. Once you have a handle on what to do move to step 3.

3. Apply what you've learnt and DO IT.

4. Do it again.

5. Do it again.

6. Smile, enjoy the results and the sense the achievement in getting what you want simply by the power of your own actions.

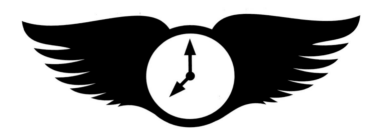

It's often said that 'Time Flies'. I'd certainly agree! I'd add that the older I get the faster time seems to pass! Make the most of your time, do things you enjoy, spend it with people who's company you enjoy and help the people in your life. Time is the one thing you can't buy more of and you can never get it back. However certain lifestyle choices can improve your chances of living longer and of also retaining your health through these extra years.

There is no guarantee that exercise will definitely make you live longer, but it tips the balance in your favour! Personally, I'd rather know I'm doing what I can to affect the things that can be affected and not leaving things to chance.

I can truly vouch for the power of exercise and its power in keeping me feeling young. Exercise - DO IT! Life - LIVE IT!

Every year you get not 1, not 2 but 365 chances to make a difference. How many chances do you need? How many of these opportunities do you take? How many times are you going to let a moment pass you by, whilst easily finding time to complain about the life you're creating by letting moments pass you by?

Too tired, too old, too busy? OK, some may agree with you but how come not everyone is singing from your hymn sheet? How come at least one person you know has the thing you want? How come someone you know has what you want and it was even more difficult for them to get it than it would be for you? Magic beans? Star dust? Unlikely.

The reality is the difference between the 'haves' and 'have nots' is perched between your ears. You choose your mindset. I know - it's a hell of a responsibility, right? Yet just as you actively choose not to believe, not to be confident, not to be proactive you can also choose to believe, to be confident and to GO AND GET WHAT YOU WANT.

Once the mind is 'set' it's time to take ACTION. **'Working achieves what wishing won't'**, so it's time to do some learning, experimenting and apply effort in the direction of your goal. Results have to be created and you are the CREATOR!

Today's another chance for YOU - take it, shape it, use it, make it your own.

# SMALL GOALS. LARGE GOALS.

People want things all the time. It's human nature to reach out for the newer/bigger/brighter things. New hair style, different car, abs, chocolate, the list of human 'needs' goes on and on. Using the chocolate as an example, let's break down the process that gets that sugary delight from your brain into your gastrointestinal tract. First you see an advert or someone else with the chocolate you want, or your blood sugar drops creating hunger. You then walk to the cupboard, drive to the shop or garage and buy the piece you want. So thoughts bring about the lining up of actions, these are then carried out and the goal is reached. In reality it's quite simple.

The simple chocolate example can be expanded across to other, seemingly complex, larger goals. Losing body fat and building muscle, for example, are often thought of as an absolute minefield, so much so that most of the time even though the will is there the goal is not reached. For many people there's a 'paralysis by analysis' and all impetus is lost. Which foods, when to eat, how much to eat, should I even EAT?? Should you do this diet or this newer fad or the one your friend/the internet recommends (a.k.a. 'sells')? The choice is as great as the confusion it causes.

The truth is that it needn't be that difficult. If you're looking to lose body fat choose one of the following; cutting sugar from all your drinks (hot and cold) OR restrict all fast food/junk food/take away to one half day per week (most people pick Sunday P.M. but you might prefer a week night or Saturday morning, for example) OR begin doing 15 minutes of moderate intensity (7/10) cardio after ever single weights session. Keep it simple and do just ONE. Then next week add in another of these modifications, the week after the 3rd. Doing these 3 things alone will dramatically improve the nutrition of 90% of people. If you're already doing these things, but not seeing the results in fat loss that you want, it's time to increase your cardio duration. Shoot for 20 minutes after each weights session and one day where you only do cardio. Once this is done it might benefit you to up your protein intake and reduce your carbohydrate intake correspondingly. This will move you toward less blood sugar fluctuations and ensuring you're able to repair fully from each session (you are lifting, right?!)

In conclusion, don't be put off by the apparent size of a goal. Everything can be broken down into constitute parts and small, achievable steps can then be taken to get you to your destination.

GOAL

# ADAPT AND LEARN

Got fat over Christmas? See it like this - you're now an expert in what makes YOU fat and can adapt your eating habits accordingly. Hurt your shoulder in your last workout? You're now fully aware of what makes your shoulder hurt, can avoid said movements and you now know to get treatment on damaged tissue. Strength dropped because you've not factored in sufficient rest days? You now have a perfect example of how inadequate rest can negatively effect your performance and you can now structure your workouts with this knowledge.

Bad things will happen, as sure as egg whites is egg whites. You can minimise the chance of negative things happening, but you can't truly eliminate it. Every now and again something will launch a spanner into your workings, this IS going to happen though it shouldn't be your focus. It's how you RESPOND to them that is more deserving of your energies and which is key!

The most important thing is what you do after you realise you're fatter, injured or weaker. Do you just carry on and repeat the actions that have caused the issue and make it worse? Or do you learn from what's happened and implement actions to overcome the issue? The choice is yours.

# BELIEVE IT
# TO
# ACHIEVE IT

Your hands are tied. There's nothing you can do. It's too hard. There's no chance. It's a too much of a long shot. It'll never work! It's all uphill. The tide's against you. Sound familiar?

It's a good job your employer, sporting hero, musical idol, Thomas Edison, Nelson Mandela, Steve Jobs, Henry Ford et al didn't have the same attitude!

The difference between those that do and those that don't is belief. The next time you find yourself complaining about your physique/job/wages/housing/etc, ask yourself have you got the belief to change it? If not, prepare to have to tolerate your current situation until something other than you changes it.

If you do find yourself in the minority, with belief on your side, you will work, learn, aspire, struggle, fight and sacrifice until you reach your goal. Then again, if you're in the minority, you will already know all of this.

" THERE IS ONE QUALITY WHICH ONE MUST POSSESS TO WIN, AND THAT IS DEFINITENESS OF PURPOSE, THE KNOWLEDGE OF WHAT ONE WANTS, AND A BURNING DESIRE TO POSSESS IT. ' "

*Napoleon Hill*

## Know what you want and get after it!

Nothing worth having is going to come to you. You have to go TOWARD what you want with determination, conviction and relentless energy.

Muscles won't build themselves and you can be sure that if what you're doing hasn't worked then a syringe or pill is not going to offer a durable or effective solution. Eat/lift/rest in line with your goal and results will come. If you don't know how to do this, learn! & GET HELP from someone who's already done it.

Fat won't just magically melt off just because you don't want it. If you could 'think' fat off no one would get fat in the first place! No pill/juice/diet/fad/snake oil/marketing will ever be more effective than 'moving more', lifting weights and appropriate healthy eating. Don't try and reinvent the wheel. The answer to your 'how do I tone-up/lose my love handles/get leaner' is staring you in the face from your local gym/supermarket/kitchen. Or come back to me in 12 months and show me what your juice/pill/fad has achieved if you'd prefer? I know what I will put my trust in!

If you knew there was a method to achieve something, that it was proven over an excess of 100 years, with no deleterious effects and used by millions of people of all ages, would you still go and look for another way?

Define your goal, make a plan (with logic and knowledge (yours or others) and execute the plan with energy and commitment. It's THAT simple and if you think not its because you don't actually want what you think you want.

## Injured?

Get it assessed and treated by a professional. Train other body parts in the meantime.

## Results plateaued?

Take a week off, start a new program and get your technique assessed.

## Got less time to train?

Learn about supersets, interval training, strip out all unnecessary exercises and condense training into fewer days.

No matter what the issue, once it's happened, it's up to YOU to deal with it. It's your ability to respond which will decide how significantly the issue effects you.

Don't let a one setback derail you. You're in charge!

CAN OFTEN PROVIDE
THE FIRMEST OF
FOUNDATIONS
FOR FUTURE
SUCCESSES.

There's nothing quite like being broke to make you appreciate money and be frugal. Illness makes you appreciate your health more than being healthy! Being alone makes you appreciate and value your friendships.

If you're currently injured or unable to train, focus on preparing for your comeback. Spend your usual training time reading, learn about training and nutrition. Spend some time talking to people who've done what you want to do and learn.

Get yourself facing in the right direction, with good people around you and a strong attitude that things can only improve. Know that from your 'Rock Bottom', you can only go UP!

Before you worry/complain about what's happening around you, consider what you are capable of changing in yourself. Chances are you can change yourself far more quickly and easily than what's going on around you.

# 'UNLEARNING' IS UNDERRATED!

The chances of you nailing everything with perfect technique the first time you try it is highly unlikely. It's wholly probable that there's a few moves/exercises/misconceptions that you could do with reassessing and altering to get you greater gains.

Personally, when I began Bench Pressing I focussed solely on 'moving' the weight, I got stronger quite quickly. Yet when I looked at the results it was clear that my triceps and shoulders were developing but my chest wasn't progressing at the same rate. Watching a Milos Sarcev clip on youtube it became clear that my technique left a lot to be desired. I wasn't arching my back nearly enough, I wasn't keeping my shoulder blades pinched and I was engaging my triceps far too much at the top of the movement by locking my arms out. Cue a change in technique at my next chest session and a drop in weight lifted of 20KGs! The rest of the day was spent with me thinking that something was definitely awry. The next THREE days were spent knowing something was definitely BETTER. The soreness in the target muscle was like nothing I'd felt before in my chest.

Over the next few sessions I continued to 'unlearn' my old technique, learn a new more effective technique and relearn how to Bench Press for better muscle stimulation. Within 6 weeks I was back to pressing my previous best weight, but now with much more effective technique and better results.

What do you need to unlearn? Do you rely on sit ups instead of doing cardio? Unlearn that shit! Do you focus on machine work and neglect compound, free weight movements? Better get unlearning! Is your lateral raise/deadlift/squat/T-bar row like exercise homicide? Get unlearning! Think that some juice/diet/pill/fad/gimmick is going to take the place of your own effort? UNLEARN!

# HELP IS NOT FAR AWAY

You want someone to control. Someone who'll do whatever you want. Someone who can work for you, earn what you want, do what you think, get the things you desire. You want someone who won't give up, who doesn't care how tough things get, who'll be relentless in the pursuit of helping you attain your goals. You want someone with energy, drive, determination and the ability to get things DONE.

Now go look in the mirror and say - "You're hired".

# GOT A GOAL?

Maybe it's fat loss, maybe it's building muscle, maybe it's improving sporting performance, maybe it's something financial. If it's a fleeting notion of just liking the idea of these things, then that's where it will stay... as an idea, solely in your mind.

If the idea has progressed into an actual desire, if you've marshalled the troops and things are now happening it means you now WANT that goal. It's not a mere dream, it's now taking form and becoming reality. You're bound to have noticed a difference between just day dreaming and WANTING.

When you WANT to - difficult doesn't stand a chance. 'Tired' becomes irrelevant. 'Cold' doesn't matter. Time distorts in your favour. Valuable assistants come along and the stars align.

Step up your game from just thinking about something to WANTING IT and see what a difference it can make!

# PROBLEMS...

The trouble with them isn't their existence but our perception of them. Often, the real problem is the way we SEE the problem.

Want to change your body shape/fitness/strength but view it as daunting/huge/impossible? Then it won't happen. In reality it's simply a matter of stringing effective workouts and meals into a long enough sequence. Doesn't sound so bad now does it? Same problem, different perception.

## CHANGE YOUR PERCEPTION

# START...

Too often people crumble and quit due to short-sightedness. A bad hour at work, a tempting snack, a spell of rain can all mean that focus is lost and bad decisions are made.

How many debts could be cleared if the focus was kept on being debt-free instead of getting to Friday and pissing the money down a drain in a vain attempt to escape the thoughts of being in debt? This only perpetuates the problem! When long term focus is lost bad decisions are made.

# ...WITH THE END IN MIND

Got physique/health aspirations? Keep sabotaging your dreams with actions or lack of actions? Instead of using food or laziness or apathy or consumer goods to pacify your inner annoyance at yourself - do the necessary cardio/ weights, exercise the required restraint, get shit done and reach your goals!

When weakness comes a knockin'- keep the END in mind!

GOAL

On the way to creating your desired body/home/career you'll be faced with a million and one decisions. Only one person makes these choices. The good news is it's YOU.

Your current situation is a result of your previous decisions. Your future will be the result of decisions you will have to make. Eat this, don't eat that? Walk or drive? TV or train? Work or shirk? Try or lie? Graft or give in?

The achievers will already know this to be true, they're already living it. The disbelievers will continue to believe life is about luck, chance, misfortune and not accept responsibility for how their own life pans out.

I challenge you to take responsibility. Want to be leaner? I'll see you on the cardio later tonight. Want to be more muscular? I'll see you with a training log, blasting compound movements, challenging yourself, training with so much intensity that it hurts.

Make decisions - they're YOUR decisions, make Progress!

# MONDAYS

Monday ain't no punishment yo fool, it's a damn opportunity!

It's an opportunity to impress yourself, your boss, your partner. It's an opportunity to do something selfless, helpful and productive. It's an opportunity to fit in one or two(!) cardio sessions, lift a new weight, learn a new skill.

Monday - just as long and just as useful as any other day - so USE it.

The sense of achievement of reaching goals is more than just the end product. Sure at the end there is the feeling of attainment, reaching the summit and completion of the goal. Yet, in addition there is also the knowledge that en route to your goal you overcame procrastination, you beat time wasting, you made numerous decisions to refuse to fail. You made a plan, set course and pushed on until the job was done.

Goal attainment is great, but take pleasure in the initiation and the journey itself!

# SOMETIMES WE DON'T 'GET IT'

Sometimes we don't get 'it' straight away. I'm a regular ignoramus at Christmas, if it's not a CD I asked for then it can't be any good! Socks! What do I need more socks for? Then something happens. The new/no good CD finds its way into my car and onto my CD player.... and... I know a track or two! Another song is one I'd heard before and wanted to find out who it was by. Another track grabs me and beats all the others, this album is quite something! Whilst listening to the CD I get a text to go out, it's dog walking time. I have no thick socks... checking the sock draw I see I have exactly the right number of thick, dog walking socks I need. Even better, they're clean, new and still have the label on them.

Sometimes we don't get IT straight away, then IT comes to life and proves its worth. I 'got' exercise pretty quickly, but you may not have. Hang in there and you WILL get it!

# WHY TOLERATE BEING IN A BAD MOOD?

Ever sat down in front of the television, turned it on and watched something for hours... that you hated? Nope? Me neither. There's no need to tolerate it, right? Get the remote control, change the channel and watch something that feels good and ticks your boxes.

So why tolerate being in a bad mood?

As much as you choose to be in a 'bad' mood, you can change your channel to being in a good mood, any time. Next time the channel needs changing do something you enjoy - phone a close friend, tell someone you love them, recall a priceless memory, cook your favourite meal, take a workout, remember how fortunate you are to be able to do any of these things!

Exercise can be your remote control. Endorphins rock!

*"The emotions you once thought of as negative are merely a call to action".* Anthony Robbins.

This stunningly simple yet brilliant observation hits a big nail squarely on the head. Feelings aren't there to cause you pain, they're there to point the way!

• If you feel annoyed about the pain in your injured shoulder... get it treated!

• If you feel bored with your workout routine... change it!

• If you feel filled with dread about going to work...find another job!

• If you feel guilty about overeating... stop overeating so much!

Feeling annoyance, boredom, dread, guilt, etc is not a bad thing, it's a message to our conscious mind to seek ACTION. Failing to act on these messages is the real failure which allows them to grow.

Millions of people have conquered injuries, changed jobs, taken control of their eating habits... and so can you!

# DIVIDE AND CONQUER!

Breaking up blocks of chocolate, sipping wine, reading a few pages, watching one episode of a series at a time, lying in the sun. With the good stuff we seem to instinctively know to split it up into so as not to overwhelm ourselves.

So why try and solve problems in one go? Break it up! Divide the problem into smaller, more manageable portions and it will soon look far less daunting. There's no need to try and attack a problem in one huge, immovable lump. Divide and conquer!

# NUTRITION & BODY COMPOSITION

# WEIGHT AND FAT ARE NOT THE SAME

When people tell me they want to lose WEIGHT, I tell them to put their hands on the area where they want to lose WEIGHT from. Guess what's there? FAT. If you want to lose WEIGHT - go jogging, go 'on a diet', go sit in a sauna! However! If you want to lose FAT then get to a gym! Lift weights to increase your metabolism and shape your body. Do cardio to burn off the FAT which is covering your newly sculpted muscle and eat regularly spaced, frequent, small meals of complex carbs and lean sources of protein. WEIGHT and FAT are not the same.

# KNOW YOUR ENEMY

It's not your tummy, it's not your stomach, it's not just plainly 'weight'- it's FAT. It's stored energy. It's excess energy YOU have consumed that your body didn't need. The first step to tackling it is to actually acknowledge WHAT IT IS! Once you do that you can then formulate a plan to tackle and reduce this form of stored energy. The longer you go on avoiding the facts the more time you waste.

# WHAT YOU EAT IN PRIVATE...

# SHOWS UP IN PUBLIC

RESISTANCE
TRAINING

IS A MUST!

'Dieting' pushes the body into survival mode, causing the break down of muscle tissue and the mind to constantly obsess about food. Training with weights encourages the body to be stronger, more efficient at burning calories, increases metabolism and changes your body shape. If you have aspirations of changing your body shape then resistance training MUST be an integral part of your weaponry to attack fat.

# SNACK SMART!

So you've had your whey and oats upon waking, lunch is chicken/rice/veg and dinner time is fish/sweet potato/veg, perfect? No, because mid-morning the burger van answers the calls of the rumbling stomach. Mid-afternoon the petrol station willingly supplies a extortionately priced pasty and chocolate bar (or two). Then before bed the hunger pangs kick in and lead you to the biscuit tin. Sound familiar?

The meals/snacks BETWEEN your meals are vitally important and will make a massive difference to your results. 'Snack Smart' and see results far more quickly. The type/amount of snack will be dependent on your goals, other meals, if it's a training v's non-training day, timing and your metabolism. Always consume a quality source of protein and clean carbs and or fats.

Oi, you, yeah you, yes YOU!

Remember telling me that YOU wanted to get leaner for the summer?

Remember that YOU couldn't complete regular cardio because YOU found it boring?

Remember that you were still pissed every weekend and remember still eating take away twice a week?

Tell me- how's the abs looking?

The chances are if YOU haven't changed your habits YOU haven't changed your body. Take charge, make the necessary changes and reap the rewards!

# SUPPLEMENT USAGE SHOULD BE EARNED

Protein powders will only make an appreciable difference if you're actually breaking down your muscle fibres with training of a sufficient intensity. Creatine will only make a difference to strength if you're actually already pushing your body to reach those 'failure reps'. Fat Burners/Thermogenics will only make a difference if you're eating/lifting/cardio is structured, in place and followed with unwavering commitment.

BE REALISTIC
ABOUT SUPPLEMENTS.
THEY CAN PLAY A
SUPPORTING ROLE, BUT
YOU MUST TAKE
THE LEAD!

No doubt there is a time and a place for international diet companies, I just can't think of it.

Do international diet companies promote the loss of weight or the loss of Fat? Does attending international diet companies give you the facilities to undertake activity that improves your health? When did you last hear of an athlete/sports person using international diet companies? Do organisations which are named more with marketing in mind, than reality, really have your best interests at heart (Fat is the issue - yet it's strangely absent from any company/scheme names - missing the point maybe?)?

For roughly the same monthly cost you can join a gym and improve your heart and lung health, increase bone density, reduce your cholesterol and blood pressure, improve co-ordination, increase strength and independence and this is just the tip of the iceberg. No 'Diet' will ever give you the kick of endorphins that you get each time you train, a 'Diet' will just leave you feeling restricted and deprived. Each workout is a measurable stride toward your goals. Join the right gym and you'll find the support and community you need, to get you to where you want to be! Lose body fat, change shape and improve your self-confidence all whilst improving your health.

For many people food choices are often dictated by taste. Invariably sugar, fat or salt will win the day and be consumed in damaging quantities and frequencies. To consistently make food choices solely based on taste is a sure path to gaining body fat, developing higher blood pressure and a whole other host of damaging metabolic disorders. Remember this; Taste is TEMPORARY! Focus on eating what your body NEEDS, not what your taste buds WANT. The changes in your health and shape will mean far more to you than any food ever can. Taste is so temporary people are convinced they must bow to it on a meal to meal basis! Cutting down on junk food etc will mean you can eat more clean, nutritious food instead and it won't be long until your body reflects the change.

It's not that you mustn't ever eat junk food, just be known that it should be limited. Setting a time for a weekly 'Treat Meal' is a method, used successfully by many. Knowing that you have a psychological break to eating clean, at a definite point each week, can help you stay on track and also give your metabolism/ strength a timely boost. Abusing the Treat Meal(/Day!) premise will likely undo your weeks worth of effort (this I know first hand!), so be sensible.

It's likely once you cut back on junk food, confectionery, take-away, etc that when you do eat them in moderation it will taste better than ever before AND you'll be seeing the physique/ health results you crave. It's a win/win situation. Eat SMART!

Combining eating according to your goals for the majority of the week, lifting weights in a structured and intense manner and cardio exercise will get you 95% of the results you can ever achieve naturally with your physique. If you carry out these tasks week after week your body can't help but change and improve. Unless you have some freak hormonal/genetic anomaly - your body can't say 'no'! Strength will increase, muscles will grow, fat stores will deplete and body shape will change. Changes will slow as you age, but the relationship will still remain.

With this in mind - I still see many people assessing their progress by using their body weight. NEWS FLASH - you won't care or need to know what your body weighs if you're following the above steps as the physical and visual changes will give you all you desire! It seems the only people who regularly weigh themselves are those that aren't doing what it takes to SEE/FEEL changes. If your training log, the tape measure, the mirror or the fit of your clothes isn't giving you a clear indication of your results then merely stepping on scales and gauging your current RELATIONSHIP WITH GRAVITY isn't going to tell you much. Somewhere along the line getting 'results' seems to get diluted and reduced down to settling for being simply either 'heavier' or 'lighter'. I'm sure you know people that weigh the same yet look completely different!

Simply put, if you're doing what it takes to see changes - you'll SEE changes. If not, then searching for some other way to reassure yourself that everything's OK and you can just go on taking it easy and not being conscientious about your food/training isn't going to help. The truth is if you're looking to build muscle then simply being heavier isn't going to tell you that you've added muscle, it could be fat or you're more hydrated, whatever it is - you won't know by using scales alone. The same goes for losing fat. The scales may tell you you're lighter, but if the weight lost is muscle then 'YOU'RE DOING IT WRONG'. Hence the flawed nature of 'weight loss' programmes.

Take measurements, pictures and regular recaps of your training log to KNOW if you're improving.

# "SATIS-FAT-SHUN"

The satisfaction of shunning body fat! That feeling you get when you get to set your belt down a notch. The sense of achievement when someone else notices that your body is changing for the good. Spying that new vein, shadow, cut, line. Being able to see your feet when standing up  KNOWING that your training/ nutrition is effective.

If you 'can't get no satis-fat-shun'... then it's time to change. Results will happen IF you're doing what it takes. First it's essential to clean up your diet, limit 'treat' food to one day a week to begin with. Some may think introducing cardio is the first step, but to introduce cardio while still eating poorly is pointless. Burning calories with cardio only to eat them back on with junk food is mind numbingly demoralising.

ONCE the treat food is limited, make sure you're consuming adequate levels of clean protein/unprocessed carbs/healthy fats. An exercise/nutrition professional will be able to point you in the right direction and a set of kitchen scales will be essential!

WHEN your food is on track it's time to introduce some cardio. Anything will suffice to begin with. Walking the dog, pushing the pram, mowing the lawn are all perfectly acceptable. Gym based cardio might be your choice, that's fine too. Start with shorter duration sessions, 10-15 minutes after each workout and look to build as your fitness and enthusiasm builds. You're likely to be going from zero cardio per week so don't jump in with 60 minutes sessions - start short and build. Train 'smart'.

Resistance training, aka weight lifting, is the rock on which your nutrition and cardio will be built from. When your nutrition is on track and cardio is in place and you are following a structured, intense training program the results WILL flow. The resistance training must be PROGRESSIVE. There's no benefit from lifting the same weight every week, strive for one more rep or one more kg each on your work/last set of each exercise.

Nutrition/cardio/weight lifting - that's all you need to focus on. Don't dress it up, don't give it a new fancy name, don't think it's any more complex than that. Focus your energies on these 3 key areas to get your own Satis-fat-shun!

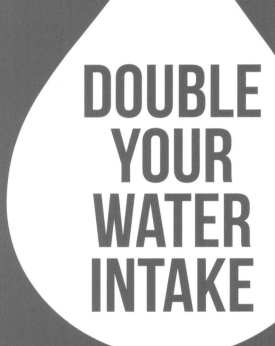

DOUBLE YOUR WATER INTAKE

Time for an experiment. If you're drinking anything less than 2 litres of water a day - today I want you to DOUBLE your normal intake. If you normally drink 1 litre, today drink 2 litres. If you normally drink 5 glasses, today drink 10 glasses. Water, in my experience, is the single most underestimated 'supplement' and 'pre-workout'. I guarantee if you're currently not drinking an optimal amount of water that when you do you will be pleasantly surprised and impressed with the results.

## Upping your water intake will:-

• Improve your energy levels to allow for more intense and effective work outs.

• Boost your concentration whilst training to allow for more focus.

• Increase training 'pump', muscles will feel fuller and harder due to being supplied with more nutrients - and not just water!

Use pure water, water with sugar free cordial, green or other decaffeinated teas to boost your fluid intake. Remember caffeine is a diuretic, so limit usage to pre-workout and ensure plenty of fluid subsequently.

Water. It's that simple, you're probably not even 'doing it right'.

# SPEND WISELY

Picture this; You're down on your uppers, money is tight and every single financial outlay has to be questioned, rationalised and accounted for.

You've got £10 left to last you for a week and zero food to eat. What do you spend the money on to make sure you can function and survive the week? Do you fritter it away on the first tasty, processed item you see. Or do you grab a bag of own brand oats (75p), some tins of tuna (49p each), a loaf of bread (80p) and a tray of eggs (£4) and with any money left a small jar of peanut butter? Thus covering all the major food groups.

The truth is the impulse decision to buy the tastier food may give some initial satisfaction, but the long term reality is that hunger will soon return and you'll be frustrated at having no more food and regret the choices you made.

The '£10' is your bodies ability to recover. The 'foods' are the exercises/volume you choose in each workout. The frustration at being hungry corresponds to frustration with results, or lack of, from exercising.

Your body only has so much recoverability. Excessively over-tax the body and it CAN'T improve, it might not even return to where it was prior to the workout! Are you spending too much when it comes to how many sets/exercises/workouts you ask of your body? Quantity is no replacement for QUALITY. Also, fill your 'exercise basket' with the basics movements and you'll be rewarded - they get the job done in less time, at less cost. Chin ups, barbell rows, deadlifts, leg press, lunges, barbell presses, dips and other large, compound movements should comprise the majority of your workouts. These movements will give you more 'bang for your buck' than the seemingly more (initially!) attractive array of curls, fly's and raises.

'Spend' your recoverability wisely. If you're not growing the chances are you're overdrawn! Reign in your spending, fill your basket with the right exercises and you'll soon be on the right track.

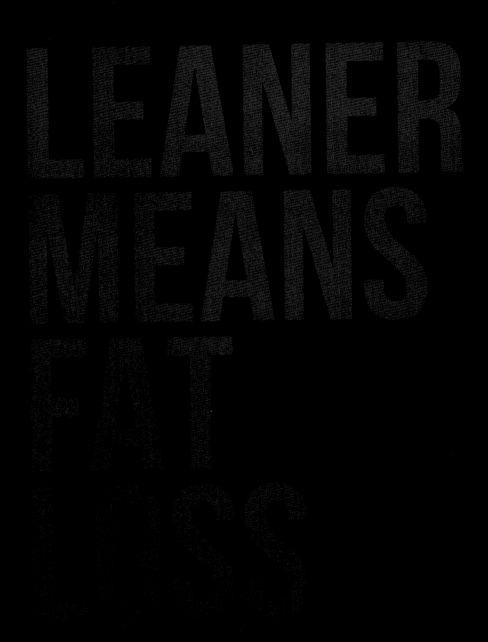

LEANER MEANS FAT LOSS

Why is it build 'muscle', but lose 'weight'? Nobody says build 'weight' because no one minds coming out and saying 'muscle'. Now when it comes to attempting to get leaner it's too often classed as 'weight', why? Is saying 'Fat' wrong, embarrassing, too honest? According to numerous commercial 'Weight Loss Programmes' it must be!

If you want to 'tone up', get leaner or mistakenly think along the lines of losing 'weight' you're basically in need of losing FAT. Know it, say it, embrace it! If you keep thinking of Fat loss as Weight loss you'll be happy every time you get on the scales and have lost 'weight'. NEWSFLASH - 'Weight' loss can be water loss, bone demineralisation or muscle loss! Just because you might be lighter does NOT mean that you are LEANER!!

If you want to be leaner, DO NOT focus on being lighter. Focus on being LEANER! This means getting measurements done using a tape measure, including high quality/nutritious food every meal, keeping 'Treat Food' to a minimum and including regular sessions of both resistance (weights) and cardiovascular exercise. Minimal rocket science involved. Know your enemy!

# IGNORE THE FADS

Appropriate EXERCISE = effective at reducing body fat, increasing muscle tissue and increasing fitness/health.

Appropriate NUTRITION = maintains bodily functions, ensures adequate energy levels, assists exercise in reducing body fat/ increasing muscle.

These are what have been used, as the key ingredients, for over a hundred years, to create the planets most incredible physiques and sporting achievements.

A long time before any marketing person dreamt up a pill, juice, diet, bar, shake, soup to rob you of your money - exercise and nutrition were kicking ass and taking names.

If you're trying to change the way your body looks, feels and performs - that's great, you're the main reason I do what I do. However if you insist on overlooking appropriate nutrition and exercise, yet relying on some pill/diet/juice you're clearly missing the point and heading for failure.

Exercising with intensity and structure tells your body to retain muscle tissue and lose body fat. Eating an appropriate, nutritious range of foods will also help supply your body with what it needs to enable you to train intensely and recover. Why would you want to look elsewhere for results, when these are proven methods?

The answer is because you're weak. You're weak and you will be preyed on by those wanting to make money from your weakness. You're looking for convenience and an easy way out. NEWSFLASH! There's no easy way out. These fads are designed to empty your wallet, not your fat cells. They rely on you failing to keep you as repeat customers.

Commit to getting started with the methods that work, that are proven and that are healthy and give up the notion that you can 'cheat' your way to the body you want.

EAT SMART.
TRAIN SMART.
BE SMART!

# SHINE THE LIGHT

Ever washed your car in the dark? No? Me neither. Doesn't make sense does it. When you're looking to spend time on something, put effort in and then reap the rewards it doesn't make sense to not be able to monitor what you're doing. When it comes to car cleaning, working in the dark you might 'miss a bit', a whole wheel, a whole panel, the job simply wouldn't get done without the ability to SEE what's going on at the time.

If you're looking to alter the way your body looks or performs it makes sense to keep a record of your work. Then you'll know what is working and what doesn't work:-

1. For strength gains - keep a training diary, a record of your Personal Bests in the main lifts.

2. For aesthetics - keep a training diary, a record of your Personal Bests in the main lifts, take monthly measurements of your chest/navel/hips/glutes/thigh/arm and pictures. Skinfolds can also be assessed every couple of months.

3. For fitness - keep a training diary, a record of Personal Bests in your main events - 1000km row/5km run/etc, take monthly measurements of your resting Heart Rate, Blood Pressure, Peak Flow, Cholesterol/Blood Glucose measurements could also be factored in.

Whatever your goal is don't try and reach it in the dark! Shine a light on what you're doing and this way you'll stay informed of how your own body is responding (or not) to what you're asking it to do. This will dramatically reduce wasted time and increase your results! Note - NO mention of body WEIGHT!

For over a 100 years Humankind has relied on nutrition from whole foods, resistance and cardiovascular exercise and rest to create some extraordinary physiques and sporting achievements. Joe and Josephine Public have also benefited from using sensibly exercise/food/sleep to change the shape of their bodies and improve their lives.

If a company comes along, tells you that your focus needs to be on its juice/pill/bars and you're tempted to be seduced by this *'you won't believe how easy it is'/'you need this product and everything will be all right'* line of marketing, do just one thing first - WAIT!

Do not buy a single potion/pill/pouch. First contact a gym, arrange to speak to an exercise professional and have a plan devised that includes resistance and cardio exercise (hey - you get to be fit and stronger too!) and a nutritious eating plan. This proven method is healthier, safer and thoroughly backed by science and real life. Apply newly learnt knowledge for just 3 months and then see if you are still tempted to spend (waste) your money on the pill/pouch/juice.

I bet you a years membership that you'll find you don't need anything other than exercise, rest and sound nutrition, like the rest of us have done for the last 100 years. Be smart!

# TREATS!

6 and a half days a week, 50 weeks a year I eat for function/effect. If it's holiday time (or treat meal) I make damn sure that I eat for enjoyment. Do I feel guilty for eating junk if it's 'treat meal' time? Nope! Do I feel guilty for consuming Oreo's, Twinkies, Taco Bell, McDonalds, Peanut/Almond/Peanut Butter M&Ms, Smoothie King, 6 different types of Skittles, club sandwich, etc whilst on holiday? Surprisingly not. It was a holiday! If I'd not taken the chance to experience these things on holiday I definitely would have felt guilty for missing the opportunity.

Remember getting in shape shouldn't feel like a punishment. Also food is one of life's true pleasures. So remember to include treats - in moderation. A skilled exercise professional can help you decide how much this should mean for you to still be able to reach your goals.

# The less
## FREQUENTLY YOU EAT
## TREAT
## FOOD

### THE BETTER
### IT TASTES

# LIMITING TREAT FOOD

Chocolate = guilt. Pizza = guilt. Glass of wine = guilt. Right? WRONG! It's not the food itself which inspires guilt, it's the frequency YOU eat it.

NO foods are 'banned', but if you've aspirations to improve the way your body looks/feels/works then you need to keep in mind how often you eat 'treat' foods/alcohol.

Limiting treat food will not only help you stop consuming excess salt/sugar/fat but also means you can fit in more 'clean' and effective whole food to help you reach your goals.

Another upside to limiting treat food is that when you do eat it, you will have earned the pleasure, there will be no guilt and you will know that this now infrequent indulgence is more than due.

There's another massive benefit to limiting treat food to match your goals. The less frequently you eat treat food - the BETTER it tastes! You will find it tastes better, means more, different flavours emerge and something which previously bought you a mild feeling of pleasure (followed by guilt) now tastes like it never has before, it tastes INCREDIBLE.

Enjoy your food, don't abuse it.

# TRAINING

# TRAIN. NUTRITION. REST.

I'm not anti-steroids or anti-supplements but before turning to the dealer/syringe/pill/potion why not get a reality check on the current intensity and structure of your training, quality of your nutrition and amount of rest you get? These 3 things are far cheaper, safer and more productive than anything else on the planet.

# FEEL GOOD

Bodybuilding is not JUST about narcissism! It's about feeling GOOD! Feeling good seeing the body working and working better. Taking CONTROL, shaping it to your will and the satisfaction from getting the results you want! Too many things in life are out of our control - but what you put on your dinner plate and how many times you lift a piece of metal up and down are your choice. USE IT! If you lift weights to change the way you feel, perform and look then you're a bodybuilder.

# FORM IS EVERYTHING

A large proportion of (male) gym-goers won't ever reach their physique goals due to a preoccupation with how much weight they lift. Instead of using resistance training to shape and build the body they get caught up with how much they lift. If the amount of weight you lift is your primary goal then take up olympic lifting, power lifting or strong man training. If, on the other hand, you would like to see your body change shape then you should be be more concerned with how you lift the weight, not how much you lift.

# OPPORTUNITIES. DECISIONS. CONSEQUENCES.

Working out, like most of life, provides you with the opportunity to make decisions. Decisions invariably lead to consequences, these consequences will then form the basis of whether you're happy or not with the effects of what you have done. If you choose to use the same exercises, relentlessly, without the willingness to shock the body then your muscles will become resilient to them. If you choose to do 'abs' instead of cardio you won't ever change the appearance of them. If you choose to stop lifting when the 'good pain' starts you won't ever reach your full muscle building potential. If your food choices are dictated by your taste buds more often than by what your body actually needs for fuel/repair then you are cancelling out what you do in the gym, instead of complimenting it. If you choose to do chest/shoulders/arms twice a week, but not train legs, you will always have a glaring weakness that makes you break out in a cold sweat at the thought of having to wear shorts!

# IT'S IN YOUR HANDS. BE HAPPY.

# INVEST IN INTENSITY

If you think crunches will 'do' instead of cardio you're wrong. If you think protein shakes are more important than consistent application of effort you're wrong. If you think you can get more from a syringe or pill than a intense set of deadlifts/squats/chins you're wrong. If you'd rather train chest or shoulders twice a week than train back or legs once that's your choice and you with your rounded shoulders, weak back and tracksuit bottoms will reap the consequences. Take charge and 'Invest in Intensity'. You're capable of so much more!

# WANT A 6 PACK? LEARN WHAT TO EAT AND DO CARDIO!

Do you train abs? Is it for increased strength to perform more effectively and efficiently in your chosen sport or is it to help prehab/rehab a injury? Then this makes sense. A strong core can help all the other muscle groups function to the fullest of their abilities. Alternatively do you train abs to 'get a six pack'? If a muscle were to use the fat stored above it then there would be plenty of fat people with chiselled jaws from the excessive eating. A working muscle does not use the fat stored above it. For most people the time spent training abs would be more productively spent performing cardio and learning what to eat and when to eat it. Train SMART!

**EMBRACE RESISTANCE**

Bodybuilding is not just about the 'Gun Show', fake tan and posing briefs. It's about taking control of something that YOU CAN CONTROL. It's about making eating choices in relation to your goals, not being led solely by taste. It's about the power of persistence. It's about creating something. It's about the single, most efficient and effective way to build lean tissue and/ or lose body fat. Surely the leanest, most muscular people know something about losing body fat and building muscle? Embrace resistance and cardiovascular training and eating small/frequent/high quality meals - you will SEE and FEEL the difference!

# TAKEN A BREAK?

If you have had a break from training through lack of will power or focus the chances are that a LACK OF RESULTS played a pivotal part. If you're getting results it's highly unlikely you will find excuses to not train or miss sessions. If, when you finally return to the gym, you use the same exercises - you will be disheartened at how much less you can now lift. If, when you finally return to the gym, you use the same training program from before your break, your body will very quickly adapt to it - as it knows it! When returning to the gym take the opportunity to use different exercises and rep ranges. Use new body part combinations and styles of training. If you just repeat what lead you to stop last time the chances are you won't be far from quitting again due to lack of results.

# WHO'S SET IS IT ANYWAY?

A 'Spotter' is there to help you complete the weaker part of a rep - the positive/concentric/shortening part, so that the muscle can be taken to true failure and stimulate more growth. If you're goal is muscle growth then you need to be completing a minimum of approx 6reps before you get any assistance. This is YOUR set and getting a spotter to help after 3 reps for more 7 reps does not constitute a set of 10 reps! 'Spotter Sets' will do nothing for your growth and show an unrealistic, weight-lead attitude. To get results for yourself YOU must do the majority of the work! Lift SMART!

If you're struggling to add MUSCLE MASS the chances are you have increased your workout volume to try and beat stagnation and improve results. Seldom is a lack of volume the issue!

Quantity cannot replace QUALITY. The likelihood is that if your training wasn't bringing you the results you wanted in the first place it's not going too just by doing more of it. Results from doing something badly are NOT going to be improved by doing more of it! You can only go so far doing something badly and it's likely if you haven't improved recently that you've reached your limit with your current quality of technique and level intensity. The answer is NOT to do more of the same. Try this instead - HALVE your workout volume, DOUBLE your intensity and know 'FORM IS KING'!

# "I WANT TO GET BIGGER"

Is one of the most common statements I hear as a gym owner. The truth is that there are many factors involved in 'tricking' your body into building muscle. Another truth is that if you've to come to the realisation that it is not happening for you then you should also realise this is down to YOUR failure to make it happen. Every single bodybuilder, strongman/woman, powerlifter or athlete that has ever inspired you has built their physique using the exact same tools you use - barbells, dumbbells, machines, nutrition, rest. If the tools aren't working for you maybe you need to look at using them differently, with more skill and knowledge. If you choose to persist with the same training/nutrition/recovery you will always be left thinking "I WANT to get bigger" instead of "I AM GETTING BIGGER!"

You've heard the saying, "You are what you eat." If you eat well, you'll be healthy and look good. If you eat like crap, you'll look like crap. Simple.

I'd like to propose a similar slogan for training: "You are how you train."

# A FEW POINTERS

Excessive use of half reps, 'warming' up with 80% of maximum weight, 6/7/8 exercises just for chest, no leg training and using almost every other muscle than the one trying to be trained are all regular sights. Am I missing something? Are these traits recommended somewhere? Is there a thriving, on-line or underground, subculture where form is mocked and results frowned upon? Why hasn't Amazon recommended to me "Get great results from shite training"? I'm going out on a limb here but I'm hypothesising - it's because it simply doesn't work.

• Half reps don't allow for a full stretch of the muscle, without a full stretch you can't fully contract the muscle. Also the body will only strengthen the range of movement you use. Train half reps and you will always have a distinct weaknesses in each movement.

• Warming up properly will not detract from your max weights, it WILL reduce your chance of injury and allow your muscles to perform maximally.

• Over training the 'mirror (or push) muscles' will invariably lead to poor posture, shoulder imbalance and eventually injury.

• Omitting leg training may seem like the right thing to do, for some, when faced with the choice of more chest and biceps or a taxing leg session. Yet consider the physical effects of only training the left side of the body. It would create a glaring, visible imbalance and anyone with an ounce of training acumen would frown upon it... see the similarities?

• If you're using the lat pull down here's an idea. Use your LATS. If employing bicep curls - use your BICEPS. If you're hitting lateral raises - use your lateral/medial DELTS. A little 'cheating' can be employed for last 2-4 reps on the work set, but this should not be your regular method of lifting weight. If you can't feel the muscle working you're either not making it work or your nervous system is not working. To test if your nervous system is working have a friend punch the muscle you're attempting to work, if you feel it then your nervous system is working just fine and your form needs attention!

If you're training includes any/many of the above ask yourself why and also 'how far can you go doing something badly?'. Alternatively, check the mirror for your answer! Train SMART!

# REPS

The basic currency of weight lifting is the rep. Reps can be performed fast, slow, in groups and on their own. Reps are your weapon to break down muscle tissue, to then lead the body to initiate the processes of repair and growth. Reps should be targeted at the muscle/muscles you're wanting to stimulate and performed safely.

Often fatigue can lead technique to break down and form becomes poor, this increases the risk of injury. It also means you are expending energy and wasting time but not hitting the target muscle(s). There's little point in performing reps that are both unsafe and unproductive. Some exercises lend themselves to 'cheating' to fully fatigue the muscle (curls, lat raises, etc), some do not (deadlift, squat, etc).

Next time you reach the point where your form starts breaking down - don't keep going! You have other options other than performing 5 good reps and then 5 dangerous reps. Common examples are turning bicep curls into a compound movement, dumbbell flys become a press-like movement, deadlifts with a rounded back, squats/shoulder press/bench press become mini versions of the original movement.

Below are some suggestions for alternatives which will allow you to maintain a high quality technique and therefore get more results from your sessions. Only use one technique for each exercise and remember certain techniques will suit certain exercises and not others:-

1. Upon reaching initial failure have a spotter on stand by to assist you with the positive part (eg the 'up' of the bench press/curl, the down of the lat pull down) of the next 2-4 reps. Ensure you pick a weight which allows you to do more reps on your own than with the spotter.

2. When you've completed your last rep with solid form put the weight down, wait 10 seconds and then restart. This should allow you to squeeze out 1-3 more reps with good form.

3. Reach your max number of reps with quality form then as quickly as possible reduce the weight by approx 15-20% and continue to work.

These techniques will keep you safe whilst training and also enable you to keep working your target muscle(s). Give them a go next time you're training and feel the difference. Train SMART!

# MALE
## OR
## *Female*

# RESISTANCE TRAINING WORKS!

Danny Tenaglia made a compelling argument that 'Music' is the answer! Personally, I'd agree in part, but the true 'answer' is Resistance Training! Lifting weights is where it's at, whether you want to gain weight (muscle) or lose weight (fat). Correctly executed resistance training will provide your body with the stimulus to increase your metabolism and use more stored body fat as a fuel. If you're male the training will also allow you to add significant amounts of muscle to change the shape of your body. If you're female, don't be concerned that you'll become masculinised or muscular - you simply don't have the levels of testosterone to build serious amounts of muscle. Any muscle you do build will help give you a shapely, stronger, more youthful looking and more efficient, leaner body.

# COMPOUND MOVEMENTS

If your goal is to add muscle mass and size to your body then free weight, compound movements will offer you the most 'bang for your buck'. Find me someone who can bench press 140kg for 10 quality reps who has a below average chest? Find me someone who can squat 140kg for 10 quality reps who has poor thigh development? Find me someone who can deadlift 180kg for 10 quality reps who is lacking back development? Easy?

Now-Find me someone who relies on endless cable and machine movements and still looks like they don't workout? EASY! These movements have their place, but not at the expense of more productive movements.

Put your trust in free weight presses, rows, chins, deads, squats, GHRs, step-ups, dips and lunges and you'll be rewarded quickly. Anyone can expend lots of energy and get nowhere, but it takes INTENSITY to build muscle! Use your allocation of time productively.

The case for the multi-joint barbell exercise is a conclusive one. It's been tested over decades by the strongest men on earth, and explained quite well by many writers on the subject. "Chopping the body up into its constituent components and then working these components separately lacks the capacity to make things change. The stress that can be applied to one piece at a time never adds up to the same stress that can be applied to the whole thing working as a system." Shush.... Compound movements are the secret.

# DOWN TIME

As much as we're loathe to admit it - we're not machines. We suffer from wear and tear and can easily get run down. Joints can begin to hurt, recovery time from workouts can increase and strength can plateau. At this point many will simply try and battle through, as if it's possible to force the body to repair whilst still training full bore. At this point it makes sense to structure in a week of complete rest. It's better to CHOOSE when you take the rest, rather than have it FORCED up you by an injury. By choosing to rest you will be in charge of the decision and of course it's better to take a single week off than be forced to take a month off through injury or systemic fatigue of the entire body.

Personally I structure in a week off every 14 or so weeks and seriously value this down time. By the time the week is up I know that my body is ready to hit the next 14 weeks HARD! During your week off you can spend time reading and learning about your body and planning your next program. This is certainly not wasted time.

# THE FREE SUPPLEMENT

If 'abs are made in the kitchen' then muscles must be built in the bedroom! Sleep time enables the body to focus on repair and then growth of the muscles. During sleep your body is not concerned with movement or exertion and so all energies can be angled towards repairing and then growing the muscle fibres strategically damaged by weight training. Underestimate the benefits of sleep at your peril.

Try grabbing as much sleep as you need so you can wake feeling fresh the next morning. Sleep should be high up on your list of 'must have' supplements!

UNDERESTIMATE
THE BENEFITS
OF SLEEP AT
YOUR PERIL

# POSTERIOR CHAIN

'Posterior Chain'- yawn, it just sounds boring. How does broader shoulders sound instead? How about a deeper, thicker torso that shows off your hard work on Chest Day? How about no lower back pain? What about Glutes that demand attention and give you the power to move rapidly and explosively? I thought that might sound better!

The Posterior Chain comprises the musculature, ligaments and tendons on the REAR of the body. Through modern living these muscles can become stretched, weakened and neglected. The opposite group of muscles - the Anterior Chain - can become shortened and tightened. This pairing of a weak back and a tight front absolutely ruins posture. Amongst the many negative consequences are the shoulders winging forward so that the chest is 'hidden'. All the chest exercises/sets/reps in the world can't out perform bad posture.

If you're sat at a desk, sat behind a steering wheel, wielding a paint brush/plasterers trowel/screwdriver/drill/computer mouse all day, then going home to then sit down in front of a computer/TV the chances are that you're suffering from poor posture, shoulder or back tension/pain and less than optimal performance when/if you exercise.

It's time for you to FOCUS on the Posterior Chain, give it the attention it deserves and needs. The muscles of the back (upper and lower), posterior Delts, Glutes and Hamstrings should be the basis around which your weeks training is structured. Failure to engage and stimulate these muscle groups will lead to weakness, poor posture and eventually injury. Ensure that your training contains plenty of rowing movements (eg barbell, dumbbell, smith machine, cable), plenty of movements that extend the hip (eg squats, deadlifts, hip thrusts, glute raises, good morning stiff leg deadlift) and those that contribute to knee flexion (bending), hamstring curls, GHR, swiss ball drag back. If this list contains lots of movements you don't know or don't use then it's time to change things up.

The muscles you see in the mirror aren't even half the story!

# NEWBIES

If you're a 'Newbie' to training in a gym it can be tempting to try and do lots of training days and body parts and exercises and sets and reps and and and and! The most important thing to do initially is create the HABIT of attending the gym regularly. This is the rock upon which all other factors are built. 3/4 times per week is plenty for you, don't even attempt to go every day - it's not sustainable and you don't need to!

Don't worry about doing EVERY exercise you can see available, select a few and work on technique. It's technique that will eventually decide your own limits. Get it right from the start and results will swiftly follow.

Don't worry about following a routine that your mate is doing. That routine is (possibly) suitable for them - NOT for you. They 'might' need 4 exercises for their chest to cause enough tissue damage to stimulate growth, you do NOT. Start with a volume suitable for you. Pick one or two exercises for each large body part (Legs/Back) and one for the others (shoulders/chest/biceps/triceps/calves) each time you train them - no more than twice per week. Complete 2/3 sets for each exercise.

Over time your volume of exercises and sets can increase. As your body becomes more resilient to training you can increase the volume and intensity to ensure your progress continues.

You might have 50 years of training ahead of you - don't rush to do things badly at the beginning!

# RESTING

Know the difference between 'resting' and 'stopping'. Resting is planned respite, it allows for healing, recovery and improvement. Resting is critical to any living thing and is an integral part of the cycle that brings about positive changes in our energy, strength and endurance levels. Holidays, weekends, sleep and time between sets are all examples of resting.

Stopping is voluntary or involuntary. Voluntary stopping may happen through laziness, a lack of motivation or removal of desire. Involuntary stopping can happen through injury or if a serious life event occurs.

Know the difference - Stopping can be avoided, in most scenarios by setting goals, structuring your effort and rewarding your results. Resting is smart and should be structured in to all program's to allow the body to adapt and prevent over-training/injury.

Train smart. Rest but don't stop!

# ANABOLIC/ANDROGENIC STEROIDS

Across the world millions of people exercise in gyms. The reality is that a percentage of this number will also be taking Anabolic/Androgenic Steroids. A minute fraction of these people will see results so spectacular that they are able to earn a living from the resulting physique, either as a professional or as a sponsored athlete. Others that respond not quite as emphatically will still display a well developed, advanced and impressive physique. The reality is that most people who resort to AAS will advance in strength and bodyweight to a small extent with each course, then quickly regress at the courses cessation to the point where they were when they started. Most users of AAS will not even surpass the effort of the more gifted/focused natural trainer.

Why this discrepancy in results? Sure, some of the imbalance is down to genetics, but this doesn't explain the overwhelming difference. The elite of the assisted world improve cycle after cycle, adding strength and layering muscle upon muscle. So why doesn't everyone that takes AAS get the same results?

The reality is that too often those that train and take AAS believe the AAS to be the most important part of the equation. The fact is that if you weren't seeing at least modest results from training without AAS when you do undertake a cycle the resulting improvements will be only slight and definitely temporary. Most gains will be lost at the end of the cycle and you'll be back at square one, but a few pounds lighter.

The focus of anyone's energies, whether assisted or natural, should ALWAYS be the foundational elements of TRAINING (structure and intensity), NUTRITION (what/when/how much/how often) and RECOVERY (sleep/rest days/naps/time off). If you're not taking care of these elements you're not taking care of yourself. There is no vial or pill that can outperform these crucial factors when it comes to importance. The 'secret' behind successful assisted bodybuilders is their commitment to these factors plus AAS. The 'secret' behind successful natural trainees is their commitment to these factors. The common themes behind success will always be Training, Nutrition and Recovery.

Whatever path you choose I strongly suggest you build a NATURAL FOUNDATION, find out what works without AAS. By doing so you'll have a true understanding of how your body works, what your body responds well to and if you later choose to use AAS you'll know how to maximise the benefits compared to their risks.

# BAD FORM

Am I missing something? Is it written on a ancient tablet somewhere, that I don't know about? Is there a secret scroll in a far away cave I've never seen? Where does the information or inclination to train so badly come from? Is it passed down in a mystic initiation behind the closed doors of an illicit fraternity?

**If you;**

- 'Warm-up' with more than 60% of your max weight, you confuse the f**k out of me.
- Get a 'spot' on anything but the last 2-4 reps of your last/heaviest set, you baffle me.
- Think that it's ok to train chest twice a week, yet legs not once, and complain about not 'getting bigger'- you bewilder me.
- Consistently use more exercises and sets for your biceps than the entirety of your legs - you truly do leave me scratching my head.
- Turn a seemingly simple exercise like a Lateral Raise into a bastardised hybrid of calf raise, glute thrust, shrug and rear fly you've got me befuddled with your logic.

Where do these notions come from? I'd like to meet the originator and check out their physique, they must be a human tank!

Personally I put my faith in people that look like they know what they're doing and have a track record of successful pupils/clients/teachings. Dan John, Mark Rippetoe, John Meadows, Charles Glass, Hany Rambod all have a solid history of sound teachings and I've never seen any of them recommending ANY of the above.

It's not a warm up if you're using anything close to your max, a warm up should, by definition, be LIGHT and progressive. 'Start light, get it right!'

If you're not lifting the weight, you're not going to grow. Simple.

If you're not trainings legs you're missing out on the biggest growth/appetite/metabolic kick you can naturally give your body.

If you think a single small muscle deserves as huge amount of volume - try it with your calves and see how it feels! And by the way, how many inches has your routine put on your arms?

If you think just lifting the maximum weight possible is key - go home, read, learn, come back another day.

# DO YOUR HOMEWORK

In his 2008 book 'Outliers', Malcolm Gladwell proposed the theory that it takes 10,000 hours of practice to become an expert, in any field, from basketball to piano playing. Of course it may take far longer if your hours of practice are not of a high quality. It may never happen if your hours of practice are spent doing things incorrectly, are lacking intensity or are not followed up with the right amount of recovery.

The pressures of modern life and the media can make it feel like it's necessary to have everything yesterday! So how can we speed up the arrival of the results we want?

1. **Knowledge!** If you think squatting will ruin your knees, don't know what muscles the squat works or don't know what a squat is, then it's time to get some learning done. Think that oats are classed as a high-protein food? Think that bacon comes from cows? Curious as to how many calories in a glass of water? (Honestly- these are questions I've been asked). If you don't know the first thing about exercise or nutrition (or even if you do) then get reading some websites (T-Nation!), some worthwhile books, observing some advanced trainees and invest in some time with a professional (Personal Training).

2. **Consistency!** Training smart is all well and good, but to see real results you must layer week after week after week on top of each. Visible results don't happen overnight, but give it several weeks of smart and consistent training and you will see changes happening.

3. **Intensity!** Training with logic and good form week after week, eating right and resting sufficiently are all massively important. Yet without the required intensity your muscles will never grow and fat cells won't be drained. Make sure your training is 'comfortably uncomfortable'! To push the boundaries of your body you must challenge your body to do things it hasn't done before. Lift a little more, complete a couple more reps, move a little faster, train a little longer. Do whatever it takes to force your body to positively adapt.

4. **Knowing when to back off.** You can't head forwards forever. Walls will appear that you'll have to circumvent, climb over or burrow under, all these will be quicker than trying to smash through. Sometimes a week off training is the most productive thing you can possibly do. We're not machines and intense training will impose significant demands on your ability to recover. Not allowing for adequate rest will lead to overtraining and increased risk of injury- AND a serious lack of results! If it's been more than 14 weeks since you took a full week off resistance training then the time is now!

Get the knowledge you need to train and eat for your goals, train with consistency and intensity and know when to rest and the results will flow as fast as your genetics will allow.

# AGE IS JUST A NUMBER

Ageing is too readily associated with a decline in performance and health. It's whole-heartedly accepted by most people that they will get weak, they will lose their independence and they will accept giving up the ability to do the things that make life rewarding and exciting.

Sarcopenia (from the Greek meaning "poverty of flesh") is the degenerative loss of skeletal muscle mass (0.5-1% loss per year after the age of 25), quality, and strength associated with aging. Sarcopenia is a component of the frailty syndrome - Wikipedia. 25!! Muscle loss plays a huge role in the frequency of slips/trips/falls and then the inability to recover from them, in older adults.

My gym has a number of members over the age of 60 years old. Whenever I speak to any of them, or watch them train, the first thing that strikes me is how much younger than their age they seem to be, both in speech and movement. 'Use it, or lose it' is a phrase that's often utilised when speaking about older people, activity and the retention of their faculties. Guess what- it's TRUE! If muscles are not used, they will waste. If heart and lungs are not exercised, they will decrease in performance. If strength isn't maintained through weight lifting, you will get weak!

In my experience, applying weight training and a positive outlook are as close to a fountain of eternal youth as we're ever likely to get. It's not just about more years in your life, but life in your years!

Time marches on, but it's up to us at what speed we follow!

# DO LESS BUT DO IT BETTER

Your results have dried up and strength has plateaued. You've tried adding exercises, adding more sets, what the guys in the magazines recommended, the move the big fella down the gym said was the 'best', you've tried everything! Much scratching of heads means this is a serious problem with serious frustration attached.

How about reducing the VOLUME of your training? Instead of increasing the volume of what you're doing, cut it back. Instead of 4/5 presses for Chest, just do 2 - but HAMMER those 2 presses. It's more effective to get 1 more 'Growth Rep' on an exercise than add in the work required to do another exercise. Cutting back the volume will allow you to train more INTENSELY, and it's intensity which will reignite your gains. You're not getting paid cash for being in the gym the longest, but you should be getting paid in muscle/strength/fitness if your training is effective.

Sure it's more comfortable to carry on at your current level of intensity, and just add another exercise in the hope that this will be what pushes you further on. Yet there's no prizes given out for doing a shit-load of work, half-assed! Do as much as you NEED to do to get the job done and do it with intensity. Do LESS, but do it BETTER. Crank up the intensity and keep your TECHNIQUE tight. Intensity multiplied by quality technique = RESULTS!

# THE ONLY PERSON YOU SHOULD STRIVE TO BE BETTER THAN....

# ...IS WHO YOU WERE YESTERDAY!

# FOCUS

Don't worry about what's being lifted on the next bench. Don't concern yourself with looking at what others are pushing. Don't divert any of your attention to how many plates someone else is pulling.

The chances are if you focus on keeping up with someone else your form will worsen and you'll be tempted to go for any kind of rep and not quality, muscle-stimulating reps. A reduction in the quality of what you do will never succeed long term!

Instead, focus on improving what YOU are doing by 1kg or 1 or 2 reps more than your last session. Making this your focal point will bring huge improvements in a shorter length of time.

The only person you should strive to be better than is who you were yesterday!

# START LIGHT

You may find it uninspiring contemplating preparing your biceps and shoulders to hit Chin/Pull Ups. You just want to get on with main exercise, right?! Wait until you've got a strained/torn biceps and aren't able to do anything with them! Then you'll know the reason behind warming-up.

You might find it boring going through the gears, building up to your heavy set in pressing movements, why not just jump in at heavy weight? When you've had a pec/tear strain and can't bench a thing you'll grasp why it makes sense to start 'light' and work up to 'heavy'.

You might not yet know why you see others doing leg extensions before squatting/pressing, lateral raises prior to shoulder pressing or strange looking rotator cuff preparation - so learn! Their value is significant.

Before you even think about 'results' you should think about 'safety' and when it comes to training 'preparation' is integral to safety. If you want your body to change/improve/strengthen you must be willing and able to consistently push it to its limits. To be able to work consistently and intensely you have to be injury-free! Just 120 seconds of preparation prior to lifting weights will significantly improve your results, reduce your risk of injury and increase your lifting longevity. Training harder, safer and for longer means more results, more quickly!

Go through the gears when lifting, DON'T jump in at a heavy weight. Starting too heavy will hasten an injury and reduce how much you can lift on your heaviest set! Start light, get it right!

# IMPROVE YOUR WEAKNESSES

When it comes to the battle for our attentions, our Strengths usually win over our Weaknesses. We love to focus on what we're good at. Excelling feels much better than struggling. Until you realise that making your strong points even stronger, means your weak points become even more glaring and leave them lagging further behind.

Improving weak points will bring you more rewards. Think of it like this - you have an area you are strong in. This area is, let's say, 85% as developed as it's ever going to be. Therefore it can only be improved 15% more until it reaches its maximum development. Now, take a weak point that is only 40% developed and this can be improved by a whopping 60%. This huge jump will bring significantly more overall improvement to the big picture.

Got great Bi's? Now bring your Tri's up to match, then see how good your arms look! Happy with your strength, but not so content with your (fl)abs? Get rocking the CV equipment after each weights session and you'll soon be leaner AND strong! Lean but inflexible? Introduce some flexibility work in between sets and you'll be using up 'dead time' and improving an important area of your fitness.

# THERE'S ALWAYS A WAY

"I just can't get any bigger/stronger/leaner", complaints I've heard more than a few times from frustrated gym members. They baffle me. How do you know you can't lose fat/build more muscle/bench 140kg - when you've never done what it takes to do these things? You presume that what got you to your current level of body fat/muscular size/benching 100kg will be sufficient to get you further. Wrong!

The techniques, intensity and application that got you to where you are now may have to carry-over to where you want to be in the future. Yet the chances are that you're going to need to DO DIFFERENT to get DIFFERENT. CHANGE takes CHANGE.

"I can't seem to get any bigger"- have you tried adding an extra days rest in or cutting back your volume? Have you tried changing your routine or asking someone to mentor you or increasing your training intensity?

"I can't get leaner"- have you tried carb cycling, or Interval Training for your cardio? You're doing cardio right? Have you had your diet inspected by a professional? Have you even gone 6 days without ANY junk food yet?

Don't write yourself off as being incapable of achieving something before you've given yourself EVERY opportunity to reach that goal!

# THE BACK

Tonight's menu consists of pull downs, wide chins, barbell rows, cable rows, D/B pullovers and deadlifts! If these names seem alien to you it's probably time you picked up a book or got some form of help.

Who doesn't love Back Day? Those that don't understand the Power of the Back side! It's not all about the Pecs and Guns, the Back is the real hero! How much Back training do you have behind you?

A strong back is rarely injured! That lower back injury you've got would "probably" not be there if your back was strong enough to take what injured it in the first place.

Sit/stand full upright and pull your shoulders back/down - that's your Back working like it should - now check out how much better your Chest looks and whilst you're at it your general height/depth/width. Yeah - your Back did that!

A strong well developed Back will enable you to work your Chest and many other muscle groups intensely. Nobody is Benching/Overhead Pressing their maximum potential with a weak Back that's unable to hold the Shoulders/Torso in place.

A strong/developed Back will give your overall appearance much more balance. Look good from 360 degrees.

Back training is intense, many muscles interplay and much weight can be lifted - therefore it's a great calorie burner.

Couple this with the Backs capacity to build muscle and you've got a potent fat-burning furnace hanging off the back of your ribs. U.S.E. it!

Back training will strengthen many other ancillary muscles - forearms, hamstrings and biceps will all be taxed through using a variety of moves on Back Day.

Back training done correctly, is the most important body part you have. Done incorrectly, you're in trouble, respect the spine!

Thank you for reading.